TIME

SPECIAL EDITION

Beautiful Phenomena

Discovering Nature's Most Exotic Wonders

The aurora borealis, in the form of brilliant ribbons of colored light, dances in the sky over Norway. The northern lights are the visual manifestation of the interplay between Earth's magnetosphere, which is strongest at the planet's two poles, and the charged particles of the solar wind.

Contents

A time-lapse sequence shows a total eclipse of the sun in Queensland, Australia, in 2012.

An annular eclipse of the sun, which is slightly less than total, was visible over a swath of the American West on May 20, 2012.

This photo leads to an augmented-reality experience through the Time Special Edition App.

Download the free app, press "experience," and then point the camera of your phone or tablet to capture the photo. Make sure volume is on.

The Solar Eclipse, 2017

Ancient civilizations worshipped the sun, with good reason. The closest star gives us illumination and warmth, and our calendar traces Earth's 365-day circuit—although those long-ago sun worshippers thought the star was circling our planet, rather than vice versa. For centuries, solar eclipses were fearsome events, impossible to explain or predict. Today we understand the mechanics behind an eclipse, but scientists still anticipate them as a chance to learn more about the workings of the star that sustains us. For millions more of us, a solar eclipse is an opportunity to witness one of nature's most awe-inspiring phenomena. The shadow created by the total eclipse of Aug. 21, 2017, will traverse the entire width of the U.S.—and millions of us will turn our eyes to the heavens, sharing the wonder and awe, if not the sacred dread, of our distant ancestors.

The Allure of Totality

Exploring the lore, legend and improbable cosmic mechanics behind total solar eclipses

By Jeffrey Kluger

The moon was not placed in space for our entertainment. In fact, it was placed there by accident, most astronomers believe, as the product of a nearly mortal blow Earth sustained more than 4 billion years ago, when our planet was sideswiped by a Mars-size planetesimal speeding through local space. That collision produced a massive debris cloud that eventually coalesced into our moon. The sun didn't pop into being for our enjoyment either; it spun down out of a cloud of primordial dust and gas, just as Earth itself did. Not much glamour or drama in all of that.

Yet now and then, the debris ball that is the moon passes in front of the dust ball that is the sun and produces the glorious phenomenon we know as a solar eclipse. Even for scientists, there can be a temptation to see the eclipse as something intended to thrill, a sky show put on for the only species in the solar system able to appreciate it.

Consider that the sun is about 400 times the diameter of the moon, which would make it awfully hard for the lunar disk to fit so perfectly over the solar one—except that the sun is also about 400 times as distant, meaning that the two bodies appear to be the same size in our sky. Consider the way the ragged lunar mountains, which are impossible to see from as far away as Earth, form a sawtooth pattern at the leading edge of the moon, through which the last of the sun's light streams in the moments before a total eclipse is complete, creating the brilliant burst of light astronomers call the diamond-ring effect.

And consider, too, the rarity of the eclipse. At some

Viewers at Ocean Beach in San Diego observe an annular eclipse of the sun on Jan. 4, 1992.

First Contact

These time-lapse photos capture the stages of a total solar eclipse on March 9, 2016, in Palu, Indonesia. The moment when the moon's disk is first visible is called "first contact"; eventually the lunar transit trims the solar disk into a crescent. Observers feel a gradual loss of heat and light, and the colors of the landscape dim.

Second Contact and Maximum Eclipse

The second photo shows the diamond-ring effect, as the moon extinguishes all but one last ray of light from the sun's face, or photosphere. Scientists call the onset of totality "second contact," as the sun's corona becomes visible. The period of totality is generally only two to three minutes long, and it is the height of the experience.

point on the planet a total solar eclipse will occur every 18 months, but at any particular spot—the spot where you live, say—it will happen just once every 350 years or so. When an eclipse does occur, totality never exceeds a mere seven minutes, 30 seconds—and it's usually much shorter. Then the show's over for another three and a half centuries. Frequency cheapens the currency of any spectacle; by that measure, a total solar eclipse is priceless.

Even to modern humans, long since past the fear that the disappearance of the sun in the middle of the day is a curse or a blight or the work of a winged dragon eating the solar fires to replenish its own, there is something deeply unsettling about the sight of an eclipse. The sky darkens, which it does every day, but to a shade of blue and then black and blue that occurs at no other time. The dimming of the light means a cooling of temperatures, and a portentous lick of wind may come up as the eclipse reaches totality. Crickets and night birds, knowing light and dark far better than they know fear or superstition, begin to chirp and sing at the wrong time of day.

The sense that all of this is off, all of this is wrong, is something that our rational brains, which are still operating on neurological software that was written when we humans were on the savannas, can't shake. There is a reason the Lydians and the Medes ended their war in 585 B.C., when a total eclipse darkened the sky and convinced the combatants that it was a sign of disapproval over the ongoing fighting. There is a reason the English saw an unhappy cause and effect between the eclipse of

Aug. 2, 1133, and the death of King Henry I, even though Henry died more than two years later. That the loss of a king could be foretold by the loss of the very light in the sky made a certain kind of 12th-century sense.

Eclipse Equations

For all of that, though—for all of the loveliness, spookiness and historical impact of a solar eclipse—there is a cold, reductionist science behind it. The moon's brief passage between Earth and the sun is simply the inevitable result of the wheels-within-wheels design of our solar system. The brevity of the phenomenon derives from the fact that the wheel on which the moon rides circles Earth at a zippy 2,288 miles per hour. No sooner has the moon approached and obscured the sun than it is gliding on past it.

Of course, if the moon circles Earth once every 27.32 days, an eclipse ought to occur on that same near-monthly schedule too. But the celestial mechanics are more complicated than that. The moon's orbital plane is inclined relative to Earth's equator, meaning that some of the times the moon crosses the path of the sun, it actually appears to sail above it, while at other times it crosses below it. It is only when the moon passes the sun at the same time it crosses Earth's own orbital plane that an eclipse occurs.

Even when the alignment is correct and the planes intersect, the eclipse that occurs may not be total. That's because the moon's orbit around Earth is an ellipse, not

Third Contact

In the third phase of an eclipse, totality ends and the sun's face slowly gains in size. The retreat is heralded by the reappearance of Baily's beads, the bright spots of light filtering through lunar valleys initially seen during first contact. The corona is no longer visible, and the stars seen during totality wink out.

Fourth Contact

As the moon completes its transit of the sun's face, scientists wait for the finale of the heavenly light show: fourth contact, when the moon's disk has completed its transit and can no longer be seen. On the ground, the landscape returns to normal. Show's over, folks ... nothing to see here anymore ... move along!

The Greek historian Herodotus chronicled the appearance of an eclipse in 585 B.C. that led two warring armies to stand down, as depicted in this vintage illustration.

a circle. The moon's average distance is almost 239,000 miles, but its perigee, or closest approach to Earth, is about 225,000 miles, and its apogee is about 252,000. A moon at apogee appears smaller than a moon at perigee, and if an eclipse takes place during one of those high-flying periods, the 400-400 balance between the size of the sun and moon and the distance separating them is thrown off. That results in what's known as an annular eclipse—with the moon gliding in front of the sun but never completely obscuring it, permitting a lot of solar glare that spoils the effect. As many as 73% of the moon's transits of the sun occur when the moon is too distant from Earth to allow a true total eclipse to occur.

If everything does line up perfectly—if a total solar eclipse is going to make landfall—it's best to arrive at your viewing site as early as you can, because seating will be limited. An astronaut in orbit looking down on Earth during a total eclipse would see the entire event as nothing more than a circular shadow on the ground, measuring from 70 to 155 miles across, cruising from west to east at high speed. You must be in the path of that circle to witness totality. The August 21 total eclipse will make the coast-to-coast transit of the U.S. in just an hour and 33 minutes. The partial eclipse that precedes and follows it adds more viewing time overall, but the best portion of the experience is short-lived.

9

LIGHTS ALL ASKEW IN THE HEAVENS

Men of Science More or Less Agog Over Results of Eclipse Observations.

EINSTEIN THEORY TRIUMPHS

Stars Not Where They Seemed or Were Calculated to be, but Nobody Need Worry.

A BOOK FOR 12 WISE MEN

No More in All the World Could Comprehend It, Said Einstein When His Daring Publishers Accepted It.

In 1919 the London *Times* hailed British astronomer and physicist Arthur Eddington (right), who conducted observations of a solar eclipse that proved physicist Albert Einstein's 1915 general theory of relativity, which holds that gravity bends light.

Privileged Visions

Still, a lot can happen in those brief intervals. During the total eclipse of Aug. 18, 1868, French astronomer Jules Janssen studied the prominences—or flames and flares—that dance around the edges of the sun's blacked-out disk and, looking through a spectroscopic prism, saw the signature of helium, thus discovering the second-lightest element in the universe before it had even been found on Earth. Much more significantly, on May 29, 1919, British astronomer Arthur Eddington used a total eclipse to prove one of the premises of Einstein's general theory of relativity—that gravity will bend light by a specific, predictable amount. Months before the event, Eddington measured the precise position of the Hyades star cluster. Then, on May 29, when the sun was blacked out and the stars popped into view, he measured it again—and it was different by a factor perfectly consistent with the bending Einstein had predicted in his famed 1915 theory.

"REVOLUTION IN SCIENCE. NEW THEORY OF THE UNIVERSE: NEWTONIAN IDEAS OVERTHROWN," wrote the *Times of London*, breathlessly but mostly accurately, the morning after the discovery was announced. Newton did survive—but his work was forever altered by a later scientist who saw much farther, much deeper into the universe.

That, in some ways, illustrates one more gift of the solar eclipse: that it allows for two different kinds of vision—the aesthetic and the insightful, the glimpse of beauty and the glimpse of the workings of the cosmos itself.

Part of the terror and charm of eclipses used to be that they came utterly unexpectedly. "On the day of the new moon, in the month of Hiyar, the Sun was put to shame and went down in the daytime, with Mars in attendance," wrote a surely surprised observer in a Mesopotamian account of the eclipse of May 3, 1374 B.C. Now, however, our ability to reverse-engineer the turning of the cosmic wheels means we can pinpoint the precise date of past eclipses, and it also means we can run the wheels forward and predict all of the ones that are still to come.

There is a loss in that—in the elimination of some of the wonder at the universe's seeming caprice. But there's a great gain too. An eclipse we know is coming is an eclipse we can be ready to watch. And to watch it is to be changed forever—and for better.

Jeffrey Kluger is a senior science writer for TIME. *He is the author of* Apollo 8: The Thrilling Story of the First Mission to the Moon, *published in May 2017, and, with Jim Lovell,* Apollo 13 *(original title:* Lost Moon), *the basis for the 1995 film* Apollo 13.

Coronal loops

The roughly circular structures that fan out from the star's surface are highly magnetic and are integral to the sun's activity.

Earth

This photograph captures a rare double eclipse of the sun. At left, the moon begins to cross, or transit, the sun's face. The dark splotch above that obscures the sun's top is Earth, which also transited the star at the same time as the moon on Sept. 13, 2015. The photo was taken in the ultraviolet range by NASA's Solar Dynamics Observatory, which has monitored the sun from Earth orbit since 2010.

Moon

The edge of the moon as it obscures the sun is clear and distinct in this photo because the moon lacks atmosphere. But the edges of Earth at the top are fuzzy and indistinct due to the planet's hazy layer of atmosphere.

Photosphere

The light-filled surface of the sun is far cooler than the star's surrounding corona.

Corona

The sun is surrounded by an aura of plasma, resembling a curtain of light. But why is it far hotter than the star's surface?

Exploring the Solar Corona

The sun's majestic corona—from the Latin word for "crown"—is visible from Earth only during a total eclipse. This aura of plasma that swaddles the sun is at the heart of the most puzzling current question involving the star. The sun's photosphere, its surface, is 6,700°–10,000°F, but the corona's temperature can reach a few million degrees Fahrenheit, even though it is farther from the core of the star, where its light and power are generated.

Total eclipses offer a rare chance for scientists to observe and record the activity of the corona, the better to resolve the complex question they call the coronal-heating problem. Four of the 11 experiments funded by NASA that will be conducted during the 2017 eclipse will focus on the activity of the corona, in hopes of finding clues to explain the startling thermal gap between the star's photosphere and its surrounding corona.

All-American Eclipse

Science and pop culture hook up for the Great American Eclipse

On America's two-tone political map, Oregon is a deep blue state and South Carolina is dark red. But on Aug. 21, 2017, these very different states, located the width of a continent apart, will be united by a natural phenomenon that will drain the colors from the nation's landscape: a total eclipse of the sun. At 10:16 a.m. PST, the full shadow cast by the moon's transit across the sun will pass from the Pacific Ocean onto the Oregon coast. The path of totality—the roughly 70-mile-wide area of full darkness cast by the eclipse—will then sweep diagonally to the southeast and cross from South Carolina into the Atlantic after a 93-minute transcontinental journey.

The cosmic blackout, a.k.a. the Great American Eclipse, will likely be the most-watched solar eclipse in history: 11 million Americans live in the path of totality, and another 76 million are within a three-hour drive of it. They'll be celebrating the eclipse in true American fashion, at once a landmark day for serious science and a 21st-century pop-culture festival—Carl Sagan meets P.T. Barnum.

U.S. astronomers confess they are giddy about the red, white and blue eclipse. Among them is Tyler Nordgren, 47, a professor of astronomy at the University of Redlands in Southern California and the author of a sprightly, informative guide to solar eclipses: *Sun Moon Earth* (Basic Books, 2016). Nordgren is a fan of America's National Park Service; he created the posters that accompany this story, executed in vintage NPS style. In an interview with TIME, the self-confessed "hard-core eclipse-chaser" urged readers to make whatever effort may be required to view the event from the path of totality. "The difference between seeing a partial and a total eclipse is literally the difference between day and night," he said.

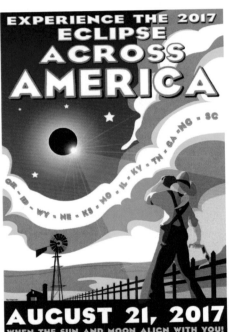

Astronomer Tyler Nordgren created a host of eclipse posters in National Parks style.

"Outside the path, the stars don't come out, and you can't watch the sun with the unaided eye, since part of its disk is exposed. You'll know something is happening, but you'll also know you missed out on the best part of an event that can be life-changing. Unfortunately, seeing 99% of totality is *not* seeing 99% of the show."

The skywatchers at NASA are just as excited. They hope the eclipse will help resolve the most puzzling question about the sun: What makes its corona so much hotter than its surface? NASA is funding 11 experiments to study the eclipse; six of them are devoted to solar activity and five to the eclipse's effect on Earth. The agency is also reaching out to citizen scientists, some 70 of whom across the U.S. will use specially designed telescopes to film the corona during totality. The resulting footage will be stitched together into a movie that will capture the entire course of the eclipse.

In the meantime, a nation high on eclipse ballyhoo was preparing for the big sky show. Along the path of totality, motels and hotels had long been fully booked. Officials in tiny Spray, Ore. (pop. 160), were expecting as many as 12,000 visitors; months before August, the town had rented 94 porta-potties to handle the crush. Idaho state lottery managers, masters of the impulse purchase, were peddling eclipse-themed scratch-off tickets. City administrators in Jackson Hole, Wyo., hired an "eclipse coordinator" to deal with the excitement. Eclipse glasses and T-shirts were showing up in stores, and an online gold rush spawned a host of new websites, including greatamericaneclipse.com, eclipse2017.org and nationaleclipse.com.

The only cloud on the horizon? The fear that there might be clouds on the horizon. Other than that, the Great American Eclipse was on track to be a grand and glorious national festival—from sea to un-shining sea.

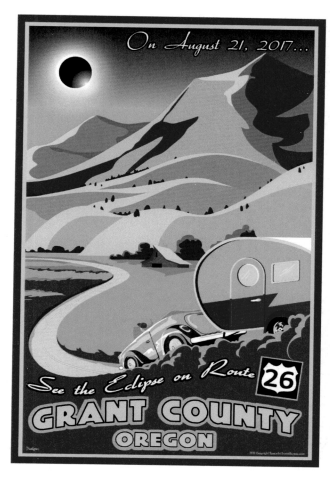

On August 21, 2017...

See the Eclipse on Route 26

GRANT COUNTY

OREGON

"THE GREATEST 2 MINUTES, 40 SECONDS IN THE SKY!"

FROM PADUCAH TO PRINCETON, HOPKINSVILLE TO BOWLING GREEN,

SEE THE GREAT AMERICAN

TOTAL SOLAR ECLIPSE

AUGUST 21, 2017

KENTUCKY

CONTACT YOUR LOCAL ASTRONOMY CLUB OR VISIT WWW.ECLIPSE.AAS.ORG FOR MORE DETAILS.

SEE THE SUN AND MOON ALIGN IN A TOTAL SOLAR ECLIPSE

AUGUST 21, 2017

FROM BORAH PEAK AT 12,662 FT HIGHEST POINT IN IDAHO

THE LOST RIVER RANGE

SALMON-CHALLIS NATIONAL FOREST

CONTACT YOUR LOCAL ASTRONOMY CLUB OR VISIT WWW.ECLIPSE.AAS.ORG FOR MORE INFORMATION.

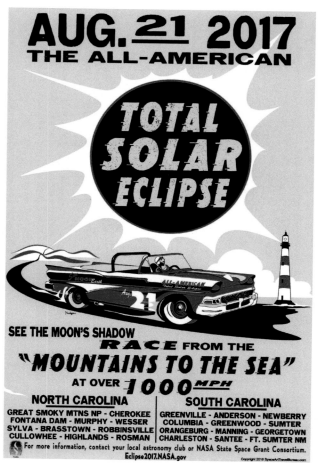

AUG. 21 2017

THE ALL-AMERICAN

TOTAL SOLAR ECLIPSE

SEE THE MOON'S SHADOW RACE FROM THE

"MOUNTAINS TO THE SEA"

AT OVER 1000 MPH

NORTH CAROLINA
GREAT SMOKY MTNS NP - CHEROKEE
FONTANA DAM - MURPHY - WESSER
SYLVA - BRASSTOWN - ROBBINSVILLE
CULLOWHEE - HIGHLANDS - ROSMAN

SOUTH CAROLINA
GREENVILLE - ANDERSON - NEWBERRY
COLUMBIA - GREENWOOD - SUMTER
ORANGEBURG - MANNING - GEORGETOWN
CHARLESTON - SANTEE - FT. SUMTER NM

For more information, contact your local astronomy club or NASA State Space Grant Consortium.

Eclipse2017.NASA.gov

A Continental Odyssey

The path of the Aug. 21, 2017, solar eclipse, from sea to sea

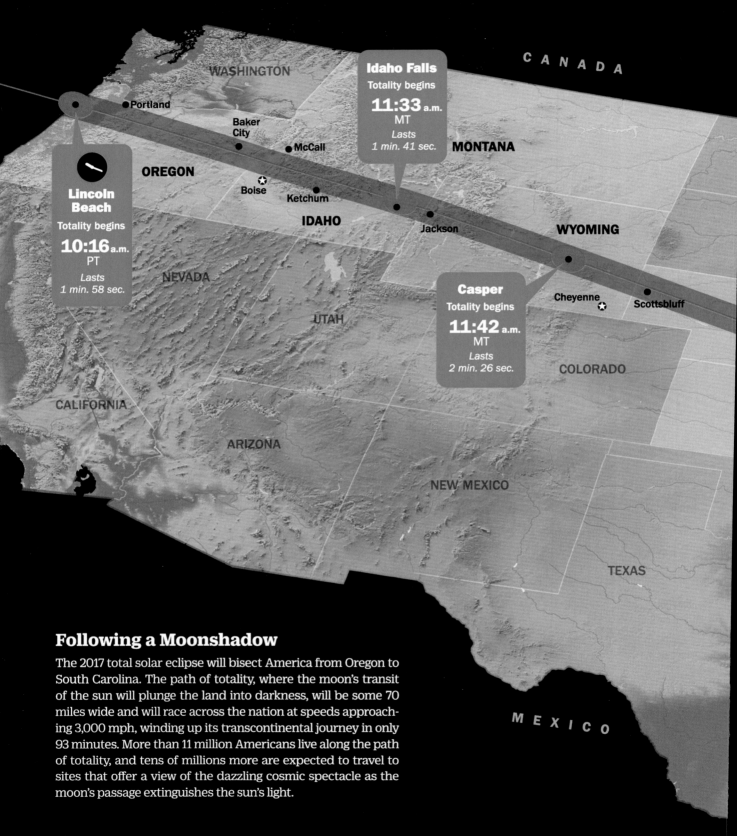

Idaho Falls
Totality begins
11:33 a.m.
MT
*Lasts
1 min. 41 sec.*

Lincoln Beach
Totality begins
10:16 a.m.
PT
*Lasts
1 min. 58 sec.*

Casper
Totality begins
11:42 a.m.
MT
*Lasts
2 min. 26 sec.*

WASHINGTON

Portland

Baker City

McCall

MONTANA

OREGON

Boise

Ketchum

IDAHO

Jackson

WYOMING

NEVADA

Cheyenne

Scottsbluff

UTAH

COLORADO

CALIFORNIA

ARIZONA

NEW MEXICO

TEXAS

CANADA

MEXICO

Following a Moonshadow

The 2017 total solar eclipse will bisect America from Oregon to South Carolina. The path of totality, where the moon's transit of the sun will plunge the land into darkness, will be some 70 miles wide and will race across the nation at speeds approaching 3,000 mph, winding up its transcontinental journey in only 93 minutes. More than 11 million Americans live along the path of totality, and tens of millions more are expected to travel to sites that offer a view of the dazzling cosmic spectacle as the moon's passage extinguishes the sun's light.

Sun

Sunlight

Path of total eclipse

Moon

Moon's shadow

Earth

A total solar eclipse occurs when the moon passes directly between Earth and the sun, blocking the solar light.

NORTH DAKOTA

SOUTH DAKOTA

MINNESOTA

WISCONSIN

CANADA

MICHIGAN

OHIO

Lincoln
Totality begins
1:02 p.m.
CT
*Lasts
1 min. 24 sec.*

NEBRASKA

IOWA

KANSAS

Topeka

Kansas City

Jefferson City

St. Louis

MISSOURI

Carbondale
Point of greatest duration
*Lasts
2 min. 40.2 sec.*

ILLINOIS

Hopkinsville
Point where sun's disk is most fully obscured

Bowling Green

KENTUCKY

Charleston
Totality begins
2:46 p.m.
ET
*Lasts
2 min. 31 sec.*

OKLAHOMA

ARKANSAS

Nashville

TENNESSEE

Knoxville

NORTH CAROLINA

MISSISSIPPI

ALABAMA

Atlanta

Augusta

GEORGIA

Greenville

Columbia

SOUTH CAROLINA

LOUISIANA

Source: eclipse2017.nasa.gov

200 MILES

Eclipsing the Sun

Each eclipse of the sun is a unique occurrence,
but some visual effects are most frequently seen

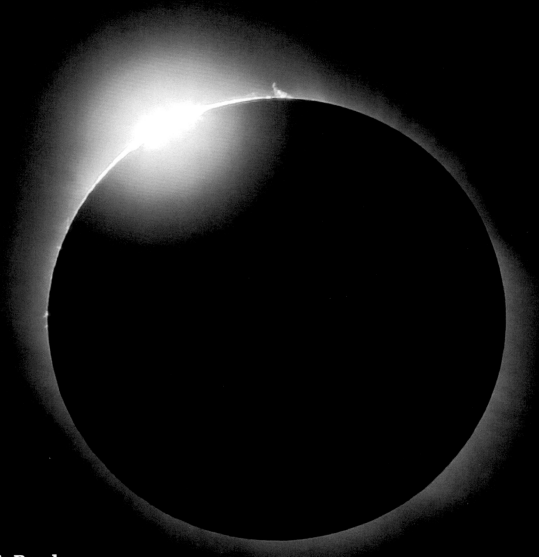

Baily's Beads

Skywatchers in August 2017 will be looking for one
of the most intriguing aspects of an eclipse—the
appearance of Baily's beads, a brief portion of
the eclipse in which solitary bright spots appear
around the sun's outer edges. As English astronomer Edmund Halley proposed in 1715 and his
countryman Francis Baily confirmed in 1836, the
bright beads are created when deep valleys on
the moon's surface allow sunlight to filter through,
creating momentary but memorable freckles of
light at the edges of the darkened orb.

Diamond Ring

Just before an eclipse reaches totality, viewers can witness the "diamond ring" effect, a brief moment when the sun has been almost completely darkened but a single Baily's bead shines through, giving the solar orb the appearance of a diamond ring.

The phenomenon occurs again just as the sun emerges from total eclipse, but both appearances are swift. The effect begins when the moon reduces the solar orb to a slim crescent and the two opposing "horns" of the crescent start moving toward each other—or, at the end of the eclipse, when the crescent begins to reappear.

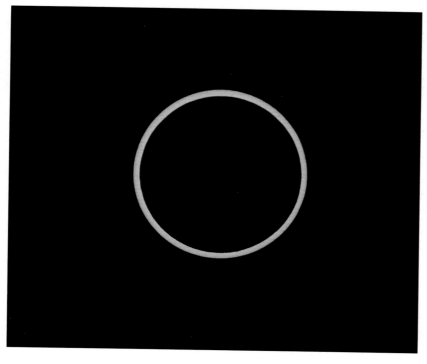

Annular Eclipse

In some solar eclipses, the moon does not cover the entire disk of the sun; instead, the star's circumference is visible around the sphere of the moon, creating a "ring of fire" effect. Such incomplete phenomena are called annular eclipses; the term means "ring-like."

The size of both the moon and the sun, as seen from Earth, vary during the year, since both Earth's orbit around the sun and the moon's orbit around Earth are elliptical rather than circular. Thus, winter eclipses in the U.S. are more likely to be annular, whereas summer eclipses are generally total.

Crescent Sunset

The well-known paradox that both the sun and the moon seem extra large when rising or setting against the horizon certainly holds true in this photograph of an eclipse in progress during a sunset. The picture was taken in New Mexico during the annular eclipse of May 20, 2012.

The eclipse began in the far eastern Pacific Ocean south of Japan, crossed the entire width of the Pacific, and passed over seven states of the American West before the crescent sun went down.

Premature Twilight

On March 20, 2015, a total solar eclipse was visible from the south coast of Greenland, across Iceland to the Faroe Islands and in remote reaches of Norway. The photograph above was taken in the small settlement of Longyearbyen, Norway, on the Svalbard archipelago. The location, some 800 miles from the North Pole, is so remote that it was chosen as the location of the Global Seed Vault, where samples of every plant seed on the planet are held to ensure regrowth after any global crises to come.

The northern lights, aurora borealis, shimmer over Iceland's Thingvallavatn Lake in 2016.

Spectacles in the Sky

For countless centuries, humans looked to the skies for guidance. The North Star, Polaris, helped orient travelers, while ancient astronomers charted the stars in their courses, believing the constellations of the zodiac shaped our fate. The ghosts of such beliefs linger: we call weather forecasters meteorologists, a nod to those who once studied the heavens to predict rain or shine. And although science has explained the marvels that draw our eyes to the skies in wonder, that wonder lives on—no amount of expertise can remove the magic that inspires us when we see a rainbow or a supermoon, the northern lights or a halo around the sun. When William Wordsworth wrote, "My heart leaps up when I behold/ A rainbow in the sky," he was not issuing a minority report.

Auroras
Particles from the sun make colors bloom in the sky

The Solar Wind, Illuminated

The sun provides Earth with both heat and light, making human life possible. But the sun also emits radiation that we are not equipped to sense—until the night skies in the planet's polar regions erupt in the shimmering displays of radiant colors that we call the auroras, after the Roman goddess of the dawn.

The lights form when the solar wind—a stream of charged particles emitted from the surface of the sun—interacts with Earth's magnetosphere, the magnetically charged portion of the atmosphere that is most powerful near the planet's poles. Above, red and green curtains of light flicker above a lighthouse at Peggy's Cove, Nova Scotia. At top right, a green aurora hovers over a German research station in Antarctica, assuming a rare circular shape.

The Science of Auroras

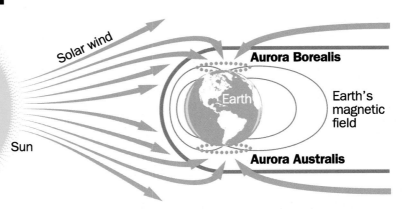

The sun blasts bursts of charged particles into space. This solar wind is attracted to Earth's magnetic fields, strongest at the poles. Result: a dazzling aerial display

Solar wind

Sun

Earth

Aurora Borealis

Aurora Australis

Earth's magnetic field

A Sense of the Immense

Unlike clouds and lightning, which appear in the lower regions of the sky, auroras occur far above the planet's surface—from 60 to 200 miles above us—illuminating the vast reaches of the normally invisible thermosphere, the second-highest level of the planet's atmosphere, as well as the lowest reaches of the exosphere, the highest level. Flickering across sweeping expanses of sky, auroras are the largest natural phenomena shown in this book.

The auroras often resemble ribbons or curtains of light, as in this 2013 photo taken in Yellowknife in northern Canada. Sometimes the colors seem to radiate from a central point, like the sun's corona; less often, they take the form of sudden beams or rays of light that rapidly switch on and off.

The northern lights—aurora borealis—and southern lights—aurora australis—are most frequently seen in the polar regions. They are aligned with the planet's magnetic poles, which are close to its geographic poles.

Rainbows

These colorful arcs are created by water droplets, sunlight—and, above all, the human eye

Radiant Raindrops

Rainbows are nature's most appealing physics lesson. Like the crystal prisms used by René Descartes and Isaac Newton in their pioneering studies of the science of optics, a rainbow demonstrates that light is composed of a spectrum of specific wavelengths, each associated with a distinct color.

As sunlight passes through raindrops, with the sun behind the observer, the light is refracted twice, first as it enters the drop and again as it leaves. The colors separate and form an arc whose pattern charts the different wavelengths of the components of light. From the outside in, the colors are: red, orange, yellow, green, blue, indigo, violet—or, as we learned in everyone's favorite grade-school mnemonic, ROY G. BIV.

A rainbow is a slippery, elusive phenomenon: when we stand close to friends and marvel at one, we are not looking at the same rainbow our companions are seeing, for this optical apparition is not really "out there," where it seems to hang in the sky; rather, it registers in each viewer's eyes (or in a camera lens) and is thus stamped by the slightly different angle of vision that is unique to each person who beholds it.

Rare Rainbows

Rainbows don't require rain—or even sunlight. At left, the spray from Horsetail Falls in California's Yosemite National Park in early evening refracts moonlight into a moonbow. When hit by sunlight at a certain angle, even a heavy fog can create a fogbow.

The photo at right, taken from a helicopter flying over Cottesloe Beach near Perth, Australia, in 2013, shows a rainbow in its full 360-degree glory, a sight visible only from above ground. From the standpoint of a viewer on the planet's surface, the horizon line, which lacks airborne raindrops to refract sunlight, prevents the bottom half of the rainbow from forming.

Below, a double rainbow soars over Kirkjufell, a mountain in Iceland. In twin arcs, the outer ring's colors are reversed from those in the primary ring, and our mnemonic friend becomes VIB G. YOR.

The Science of Rainbows

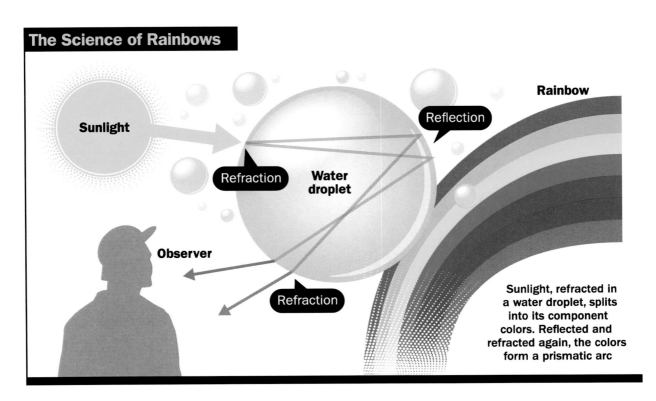

Sunlight

Refraction

Reflection

Water droplet

Rainbow

Observer

Refraction

Sunlight, refracted in a water droplet, splits into its component colors. Reflected and refracted again, the colors form a prismatic arc

Supermoons

Every now and then, Earth's satellite becomes supersized

Lunar Light Show

Spectators gathered atop Glastonbury Tor in England, near its 14th-century St. Michael's Tower, on Sept. 27, 2015, to witness a rare double phenomenon: the rising of a supermoon, which was followed by its total eclipse, as the sun, Earth and the moon aligned perfectly, with the shadow of Earth cast by the sun blotting out the moon's reflected radiance.

A supermoon occurs when a full moon coincides with the closest approach the body makes to Earth in its elliptical orbit around our planet. Result: the satellite can appear to be as much as 14% larger and 30% brighter than normal. In scientific terms, the moon's closest approach to Earth is called its perigee, and the triple alignment of the sun, Earth and the moon is—wait for it—a syzygy.

In this photo, the foreshortening created by the camera's perspective seems to flatten the tower against the moon, as if they both stood at the same distance. More significant is a trick that a rising (or setting) moon (or sun) plays on the eye. The closer either body is to the horizon, the larger it looks, because the familiar buildings, trees and other objects around it provide scale. The higher the moon or sun climbs, the more it seems to shrink in the empty sky. But if you measure the total number of degrees the moon measures in the entire 180-degree, horizon-to-horizon arc, it's just one half of one degree—and that's true whether it's at the horizon or high in the sky.

Illusions of Ice

Sun dogs, halos and sun pillars take shape when
sunshine or moonlight is filtered by ice

Lord of the Rings

Just as raindrops refract sunlight into rainbows, plate-shaped, hexagonal ice crystals
in the atmosphere can refract light into the circular phenomenon known as a halo.
The most familiar halos are those that form circles of light around the moon or sun;
because ice crystals are involved, halos are more frequent in cold weather.

When the sun is close to the horizon, a more elusive phenomenon may appear: the
ice crystals form a 22-degree circle around the sun that features two "mock suns," one
on either side of the real star. Scientists call the false suns parhelia, but these stun-
ning optical phenomena are more commonly called sun dogs. Above, a bird-speckled
halo takes shape in South Africa; the parhelion at right appeared in Minnesota.

Light Pillars

Not every interaction between the sun and precipitation in the air creates a rainbow. When the sun is close to rising or setting and the atmosphere is filled with hexagonal ice crystals whose sides are flat, the resulting phenomenon can take the shape of vertical shafts of colored light, called sun pillars.

Like halos, these radiant vertical beacons are best seen in northern latitudes or during wintertime in more temperate zones. The shafts of light shown here were photographed at Fort Wainwright, near Fairbanks, in central Alaska. In this case, they were formed when artificial light from the town was reflected (not refracted) by flurries of flat-sided ice crystals in the air; they are thus light pillars, not sun pillars. They seem distant, but that's an illusion: the columns form close to the viewer.

A Smile in the Sky

A circumzenithal arc, or CZA, forms only when a very specific set of conditions is present. The sun must be lower than 32 degrees above the horizon. The air must be filled with ice crystals oriented in the same direction, so that sunlight enters through their flat top faces and then exits at a 90-degree angle through their side prism faces. The air must be still, or the crystals will not stay in order and refract the partial circle.

But when the crystals do line up just right, the result resembles a slice of an upside-down rainbow that has been called a "smile in the sky." This formation always appears on the same side of the sky as the sun. Other circular forms, with equally exotic back stories, can be seen in the picture above of the Marquette Harbor Light on Michigan's Upper Peninsula.

Meteors

They're not shooting stars, as the ancients
thought—they are gravity's slingshot

Incoming!

At right, a camper at Siguniang Mountain in
central China—far from cities where light
obscures a clear view of the night sky—
watches the annual Perseid meteor shower
in August. The bright trails are formed when
particles of dust and rock shed by Comet
Swift-Tuttle enter Earth's atmosphere, where
they heat up, leave a swift, blazing trail
across the atmosphere, and then burn out.

The nomenclature of these so-called
shooting stars is precise: a "meteoroid" is a
small object moving through space. When
the particle enters the atmosphere, it becomes a bright, short-lived "meteor." Objects
that are large enough to impact the planet's
surface are called "meteorites."

Meteor showers are solar spectacles,
but they are not similar to rainbows, auroras
and other phenomena caused by the sun's
heat, light or radiation. Rather, it is the star's
potent gravity that keeps this space debris
in motion—until Earth's gravity kicks in to
hijack some stragglers and sentence them
to a death that leaves a glowing scrawl
across the sky.

Mammatus clouds, with clusters of pouches, hover over Georgetown, Tex., in 2015.

Something in the Air

The planet's atmosphere is the kingdom of weather, and thus it has been a subject of intense scrutiny throughout history. Considering today's advanced technologies, you might think scientists would have a firm grasp on weather phenomena. But they don't: the process of an everyday lightning strike is still not fully understood. Some phenomena are still being explored, such as the strange electrical events in the upper atmosphere that scientists call sprites and jets. Even the study of clouds is ongoing—11 new types of them were recognized by the World Meteorological Association's authoritative *International Cloud Atlas* in March 2017. One reason: everyday folks armed with cellphone cameras are helping scientists discover ever more novel and unusual atmospheric events.

Collectible Clouds

The planet's most unusual airborne wonders

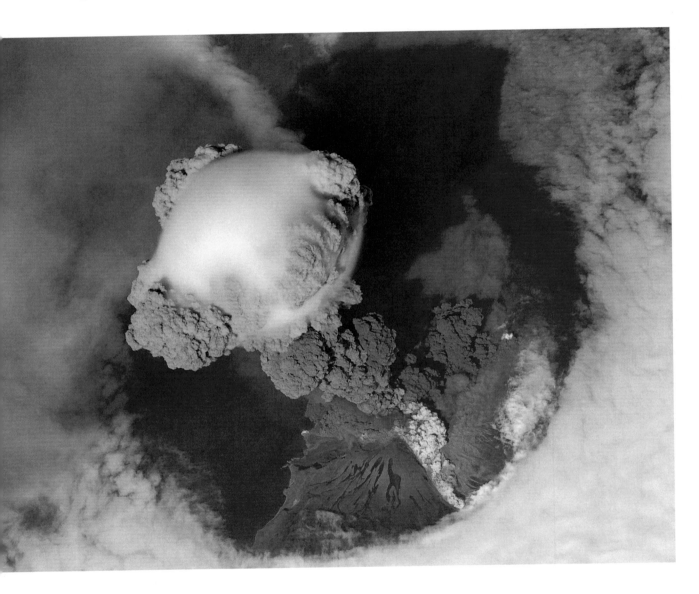

Foggy Notions

You know the usual suspects—cumulus, cirrus and stratus—so meet some offbeat and seldom-seen clouds. Pileus clouds are named after the Latin word for "cap," and they often appear on top of another, larger cloud. Because they are formed when strong updrafts of moist, warm air reach zones of cool air, they can be found over volcanoes: the white fluff above crowns an eruption from the Sarychev volcano in the north Pacific's Kuril Islands.

At right is a massive shelf cloud over Kearney, Neb. These long horizontal clouds, termed arcus clouds by meteorologists, are often found on the leading edge of a weather front.

Rainbows by the Slice

As their name indicates, polar stratospheric clouds are found high above the planet's poles. They are also called nacreous clouds because of their iridescent, mother-of-pearl appearance, caused by small particles within them that create a sunlight-diffracting interference fringe that splits light into a spectrum—the same science behind a soap bubble's colors. Sadly, these glorious, high-altitude formations help convert harmless natural chlorine over the poles into a dangerous form of chlorine gas that contributes to the creation of environmentally damaging ozone holes over the poles.

Identified Flying Object

A lenticular cloud hovers over the Lemaire Channel in Antarctica. These lens-shaped clouds, which can resemble a disk, knob or mushroom, are often mistaken for UFOs. Lenticulars generally form when stable, moist air flows over mountains or even large man-made objects and is channeled into eddies. If the air temperature is cold enough, standing waves of eddies that form on the down-wind side of a mountain or other object may condense into these unusual shapes. Lenticulars, unlike high-flying polar stratospheric clouds, inhabit the troposphere, the lowest level of our atmosphere.

Storm Clouds

Supercells, haboobs and other fearsome formations in the sky

Twister Mothership

Supercells are thunderstorms on steroids, playing in heavy rotation. These often huge cloud structures form when warm, moist air collides with colder air and creates the strong winds that constitute a mesocyclone, a cloud mass with circular rotation that causes a powerful updraft. Supercells can be 10 miles in diameter and 50,000 feet tall, and they can bring 90-mile-an-hour winds, heavy rains, large hailstones and destructive cloud-to-ground lightning. In the most severe cases, they spawn deadly tornadoes.

Supercells most often form in the U.S. in "Tornado Alley" in the Great Plains and Midwest, stretching from Texas and Oklahoma to the Dakotas and across bordering states. The colossal supercell shown here was photographed in Montana—Big Sky Country— in 2010. Though frightening to behold, it did not cause major damage.

Funnels and Haboobs

The tornado above was photographed outside Wynnewood, Okla., on May 9, 2016. Most tornadoes last less than 10 minutes, have top wind speeds of 110 miles an hour and are about 250 feet across. More-powerful storms, often spawned from supercells, can last as long as 30 minutes, boast wind speeds of more than 300 miles an hour and be larger than two miles in width.

The tornado that devastated Joplin, Mo., on May 22, 2011, remained on the ground for 38 minutes and was ¾ of a mile wide; its 200-mile-an-hour winds killed 158 people.

At top right, an immense dust storm, or haboob (Arabic for "wind"), rolls into Khartoum, Sudan, on April 29, 2007. Such storms form when strong downdraft winds gust outward from a collapsing thunderstorm, bearing dust and sand. As large as 100 miles wide and 3,000 feet high, such desert storms can take shape and approach cities with little advance warning.

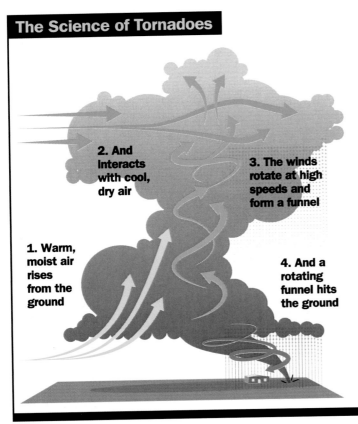

The Science of Tornadoes

1. Warm, moist air rises from the ground

2. And interacts with cool, dry air

3. The winds rotate at high speeds and form a funnel

4. And a rotating funnel hits the ground

Spouts and Whirlwinds

Storms rotating in a funnel over water, left, are called waterspouts, but the term is misleading; they are largely composed of air rather than water. Whirlwinds, or dust devils, above, are funnel-shaped, but they are not born out of clouds. Their rotation begins on the ground when hot and cold air masses collide and begin to spin.

Lightning

Shocking but true: scientists still don't fully understand these electrifying events

Striking Sparks

"Thunder is good, thunder is impressive; but it is the lightning that does the work," said noted atmospheric scientist Mark Twain. For most of us, who may never witness an aurora or a volcanic eruption or an earthquake, a major lightning strike is the closest we come to observing planetary forces in their most powerful form. Each bolt of lightning in this photograph, taken on the island of St. Barts in the Caribbean, is a single spark of electricity that can heat up the surrounding air to 50,000°F. That heat forces the air to expand, creating the spectacular sound wave we call thunder, whose report can carry as far as 25 miles.

As for the variations we all hear as thunder surrounds us: if you hear a sharp, cracking sound that subsides

quickly, you are close to the lightning that's causing the thunder—so be careful! According to the National Oceanic and Atmospheric Administration, lightning killed 38 Americans during 2016. If you hear thunder as a low, continuing rumble, you are registering lightning strikes that are a considerable distance from you.

Even though lightning is a familiar phenomenon, scientists still do not know how these releases of energy are triggered, for the strikes manifest more energy than we can detect in clouds. One promising new theory: the trigger for a strike is cosmic rays, inbound to Earth from space, that pack enough energy to jump-start a process called runaway breakdown, which elevates the energy inside the cloud high enough to create a lightning bolt.

Large and in Charge

The secret behind lightning: opposites attract. The storms form when particles inside clouds become charged with either positive or negative electricity, in a process not yet fully understood. Once the contrasting charges have reached sufficient power, they come together in the massive release of energy that is a lightning bolt or flash, temporarily equalizing the air.

Most lightning takes one of two forms: cloud-to-ground or intracloud. In the former, a negatively charged "step leader" forms in the cloud, while a positively charged "streamer" rises from the ground. When they meet in the middle, the strike occurs: light and heat are released; the electrical charge is neutralized, briefly; and thunder booms. Intracloud flashes, above, are much more common; there are five to 10 such events within a single cloud for every cloud-to-ground strike. All told, lightning flashes occur some 3 million times each day around the planet.

Volcanic eruptions fill the air with particles of ash that easily become charged, along with water vapor in the ash cloud that can freeze as it rises, also taking a charge. As a result, lightning often accompanies eruptions, as shown in the photo at right of Calbuco erupting in Chile in 2015.

Transient Luminous Events

Striking and mysterious, red sprites and blue jets are currently unexplained phenomena

Passing Fancies

These two photos capture a class of electrical phenomena that students of the atmosphere do not yet understand: transient luminous events, or TLEs. The key word is "transient." TLEs exist for such a brief slice of time—the one above on the far right flared for less than a second—that they were unknown until cameras fast enough to record them were invented. Above, electrical flashes dubbed "red sprites" decorate the sky over Colorado in May 2014 in a photograph taken by sprite-chasing photographer Thomas Ashcraft.

At right, a group of skywatchers had set up a camp near the peak of Shikengkong Mountain in southeast China in 2016, with their cameras ready to record the Perseid meteor shower, when—surprise!—a digital camera captured a brief, towering release of electrical energy scientists call a "gigantic jet."

Electric Beacon

Streaking high above the tops of thunderclouds over the Caribbean island of St. Barts, a gigantic jet flashed for only a brief second, but its upward trajectory was caught on film. Sprites and jets are only two of a growing menagerie of upper-atmosphere electrical discharges being discovered and classified; others include pixies, trolls and elves (the scientific nomenclature can seem overly whimsical, given the massive amounts of energy released in these events).

The existence of jets was first verified in 1994 after aircraft carrying high-speed video equipment flew over thunderstorms and recorded them. They can stretch from the tops of stormclouds 30 miles into the sky in their brief life span, far above the lightning from the planet's electrical storms. But scientists say little is understood about their nature and function.

In September 2017, the European Space Agency's Atmosphere-Space Interactions Monitor is scheduled to arrive at the International Space Station. Its five-month mission: to survey thunderstorms around the globe, searching for TLEs of all stripes and charting their appearances in two ultraviolet optical bands, as well as through x-ray and gamma-ray technology. The equipment will also search for another intriguing phenomenon: terrestrial gamma-ray flashes, another high-altitude TLE whose activities are currently being investigated.

Snowflakes

The beautiful realm of falling fluff is shaped
by the rigorous dictates of geometry

Euclid on Ice

Reader, we know exactly what you want to learn about snowflakes: Is it true that no two of them are alike—or is that an old fable with no scientific backing? To find the answer, we consulted snowcrystals .com, the entertaining and informative website run by Ken Libbrecht, a physicist at the California Institute of Technology who is the author of seven books on the white stuff, including his acclaimed *Field Guide to Snowflakes.* Perhaps it will come as no surprise that Libbrecht was born and raised in Fargo, N.D.

Libbrecht writes, "The short answer to the question is yes. . . . It's unlikely that any two complex snow crystals, out of all those made over the entire history of the planet, have ever looked completely alike." Sadly, we were unable to fact-check the professor's claim.

The snow crystals shown here display nature's classic geometrical alignment, in which the water molecules that compose the crystal are lined up in a precise hexagonal, or six-sided, array. Not all such crystals are star-shaped; some take forms scientists call needles, columns, plates and prisms, yet all of these types of flakes are six-sided. Many snowflakes are composed of crystals that connect during formation and thus may not at first appear to conform to nature's hexagonal mandate.

The Tatio geyser field in Chile's Atacama Desert is more than 14,000 feet above sea level.

Surface
Tensions

Planet Earth is a work in progress, an unfinished symphony whose lineaments are constantly changing. The forces at play are vast, and they often elude our senses: they include the solar wind, the electrical energies in the atmosphere and the tectonic forces working unseen beneath our feet. Many of the atmospheric wonders shown in this book—auroras, rainbows, lightning—are the visual artifacts of larger processes. When we come down to earth to explore the geological forces that shape our planet, we find again that some of the most compelling phenomena, from volcanoes to geysers to prismatic hot springs, are the signatures left by the formidable systems of a constantly changing planet, found where the barriers between visible and invisible forces are thin.

Volcanoes

Fiery portals to the planet's unseen, primal underworld

Ooze and Aahs

Volcanoes are emergency exits from the underground, areas on the planet's surface where its crust is thin and magma—hot liquid rock issuing from Earth's unseen, molten core—emerges into view. Many eruptions, like that of Mount Vesuvius, which devastated Italy's Pompeii in A.D. 79, are sudden, massive events not unlike the popping of a champagne cork under pressure. Volcanoes that erupt in this explosive manner are termed stratovolcanoes, for their signature cones are formed in strata, or layers, of hardened lava and rock debris.

Other volcanoes, like Hawaii's Kilauea, shown at left and above, are shield volcanoes, whose eruptions are placid events that occur in long, steady flows. Kilauea has been erupting slowly and constantly since 1983, in such a gentle manner that tourists can get up close and personal with its molten lava.

Planet, Venting

Above, a fumarole—a steaming vent that releases hot gases—is perched on the side of Mount Erebus in Antarctica, thought to be the southernmost active stratovolcano on Earth. The frigid polar environment allows snow and ice to remain on the exterior of this geothermal chimney.

You might think of a fumarole as the kid brother of a major volcano. Rather than acting as a vent for magma from beneath the planet's crust, a fumarole allows hot, gassy air from the superheated rocks below the ground to escape into the atmosphere. Fumaroles are commonly found along tectonic rifts, along with mineral springs, geysers and similar surface manifestations of the inner workings of the planet.

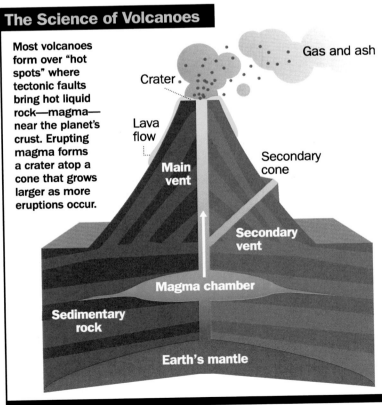

The Science of Volcanoes

Most volcanoes form over "hot spots" where tectonic faults bring hot liquid rock—magma—near the planet's crust. Erupting magma forms a crater atop a cone that grows larger as more eruptions occur.

Gas and ash

Crater

Lava flow

Main vent

Secondary cone

Secondary vent

Magma chamber

Sedimentary rock

Earth's mantle

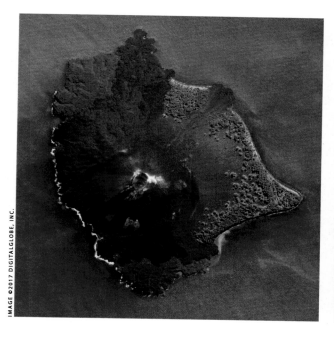

Growing Pains

The photos above offer two perspectives on Anak Krakatau ("Child of Krakatau"), a volcano that emerged in 1927 from the undersea caldera formed by the massive, planet-shaking eruption of Krakatau (or Krakatoa) in 1883. Since it first appeared in 1930, the young volcano has experienced major eruptions every three to four years, elevating its cone and forming the island that surrounds it. Anak Krakatau was roughly 410 feet tall in 1940; it is almost 1,000 feet tall today. The overhead view at left shows the emerging island around the volcano, which is now a landmass some 1.2 miles wide.

Volcanologists note that Krakatau lies in an area in which the planet's crust is extremely brittle, allowing magma to rise to the surface. The location is part of the vast, horseshoe-shaped Ring of Fire, a continuous tectonic rift that encircles large parts of the Pacific Ocean and accounts for many of the eruptions, submarine earthquakes and resulting tsunamis that afflict the region.

Color Blind

Tanzania's Ol Doinyo Lengai ("Mountain of God") confounds expectations: its lava is white. The stratovolcano produces rare natrocarbonatite lava, which is black when it emerges from the volcano's cone but soon turns white as a result of a chemical reaction when it absorbs water.

Ol Doinyo Lengai is located in Africa's 4,000-mile-long Great Rift Valley, which runs from Jordan to Mozambique. One feature of this long geological fracture is the Afar Triangle, whose unusual mineral deposits are shown on the following pages.

Geothermal Hot Spots

Gifts of the rifts are most often seen where Planet Earth's skin is thin

Contents Under Pressure

The rocks surrounding the Fly Geyser in the Nevada desert are composed of minerals released when subterranean water erupts from the geyser after being heated by a deep pool of hot liquid rock that is located close to the planet's surface. The geyser is not entirely natural, though the forces that drive it are; it formed in 1964 after an exploratory well was drilled in the area by companies seeking to tap the geothermal energy that is easy to reach in the planet's rift areas, where tectonic plates collide.

Chrome on the Range

Like a baseball, Planet Earth is stitched together along seams in its crust, where unseen forces beneath the ground are made visible, often in marvelous form. Fault lines, where tectonic plates come together, breed geysers, hot springs and fumaroles. Among the most notable such areas are America's desert West, Iceland, Russia's Kamchatka Peninsula—and the Afar Triangle's Danakil Depression in East Africa, above, where a man walks over mineral deposits that turn the ground into a palette of brilliant chrome yellows.

Surprising Springs

At left is the Strokkur geyser in south-west Iceland's Haukadalur valley, which erupts reliably every six to 15 minutes or so. Geysers (or *geysirs*, in Icelandic) were first discovered and studied in Iceland; the term is derived from an Old Norse verb for "to gush." Like most rift valleys, the Haukadalur valley is a surrealistic landscape dotted with fumaroles, hot springs, bubbling mud pools and other geological oddities.

New Zealand's Wai-O-Tapu area (Maori for "sacred waters") is a rift valley that is home to exotic mineral springs. The Champagne Pool, below, is accurately named: the hot, fizzy water is filled with carbon dioxide. But no drinking, please—the orange colors reveal the presence of the arsenic sulfides orpiment and realgar.

Among the world's most beautiful hot springs are the stepped, vertical pools at Turkey's Pamukkale springs, at right. The "Cotton Castle" has drawn tourists for more than 23 centuries.

Caves

Underground caverns offer spectacular evidence
of the wondrous properties of minerals and
illuminate tectonic forces usually unseen

Size Matters

The subterranean world is home to a host of geological oddities, but few are as compelling as the giant crystals of selenite found in the Cave of Crystals at the Naica Mine in Mexico's northern province of Chihuahua.

The cavern lies almost 1,000 feet below the ground and is very hot, with temperatures reaching 122°F. Humidity levels are often close to 100%. The heat comes from a pool of liquid magma beneath the cavern that has cooked its mineral-rich water deposits for some 100,000 years, until the solution crystallized into the selenite columns, the largest of which is about 35 feet long.

Selenite is one of the four crystalline varieties of the mineral gypsum. The scientists shown in the photo were exploring the cave in 2007. They are wearing suits designed to withstand the cave's high temperatures for short periods of time. The space is normally flooded with water; only the mining company's pumps kept it dry.

Further exploration of the Cave of Crystals is now on hold: in 2015, mining company officials decided to halt their operations at the site, and the trove of crystals is once again underwater.

Cavern Clubs

Scientists often know more about the other planets in the solar system than they do about the environment beneath our feet. Fortunately, caves are gateways to the terra incognita below the planet's crust. At top, a diver swims through a cavern that is in part both underground and underwater, the Orda Cave in Russia's western Ural Mountains. The water here is cold (−4°F) and crystal clear: divers can see details of the gypsum walls of the cavern from 150 feet away.

At right, the unique stalactite formation christened the "Elephant's Trunk" showers a mineral-rich solution in the Racer Cave, at Gunung Mulu National Park in Sarawak, Malaysia, home to some of the planet's most extensive caverns.

At left, spelunkers descend into a 3,100-foot-deep vertical shaft in one of Earth's deepest caves, Miao Keng in Wulong, China.

Minerals
Geometry and geology combine
to create marvels large and small

Landscape Painting

The colorfully striated hills at right lie in Zhangye Danxia Landform Geological Park in China's Gansu province. They are composed of mineral-rich strata of sedimentary sandstone that were deposited over eons in horizontal layers at the bottom of ancient oceans—and then thrust into the sky and turned on their side by the same powerful tectonic forces that formed the Himalaya mountains.

The island nation of Mauritius, off the east coast of Africa, is home to the Seven Colored Earths, above, sand dunes formed by the decomposition of basalt, a volcanic rock. Iron and aluminum give the soil its rich hues.

Orpiment, an ore of arsenic

Emerald, a gemstone of beryl

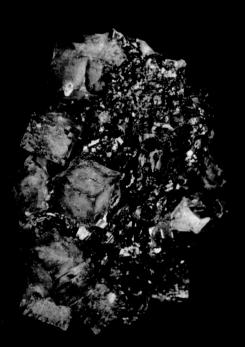

Fluorite, a halide mineral

Goethite, an iron-bearing mineral

Stibnite, a sulfide mineral

Where Chemistry Meets Art

Scientists describe a mineral as a chemical compound found in nature, a substance that is solid at room temperature and has both a specific chemical formula and a definitive arrangement of atoms. But that dry definition fails to capture the sheer beauty of minerals, which, like that of snowflakes, is often best appreciated close up.

The language mineralogists use to describe the qualities and properties of the more than 4,000 known minerals captures more of their magic: crystal structure, hardness, luster, diaphaneity (transparency), color, habit (shape) and more. For now, skip the jargon and enjoy the view.

Quartz, a crystalline mineral

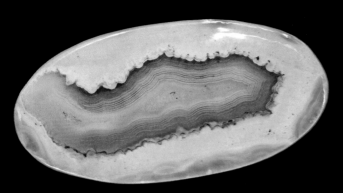

Onyx, a banded form of chalcedony,
which is a variety of quartz

Staurolite, a silicate mineral

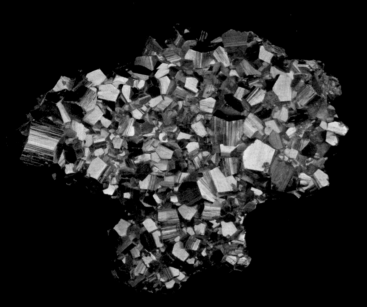

Pyrite (fool's gold), an iron sulfide

Cerussite (top), an ore of lead
Baryte (bottom), a form of barium sulfate

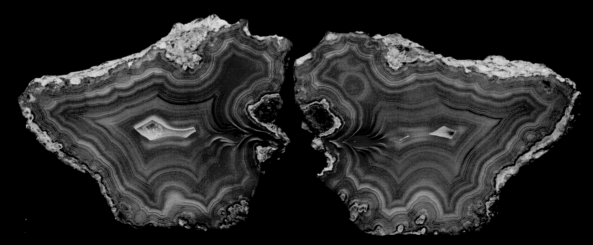

Mexican, or Cyclops, banded agate, a variety of chalcedony

Rock Formations
Our planet's topography is shaped by the strict laws of physics, and sometimes geography and geometry unite

Equations in Rock

Fingal's Cave in Scotland, shown above and at left, is one of several natural wonders scattered along coastal areas in the Atlantic Ocean; others include Giant's Causeway in Northern Ireland and the Hebridean island of Ulva. Each of these sites boasts solidified lava flows that formed hexagonal pillars of basalt as they dried, contracted and fractured along perfect geometrical lines.

At right, spherical rocks dot the hills in Theodore Roosevelt National Park in North Dakota. These "cannonball concretions" were formed by hard minerals that accumulated around a central core and were later revealed by the erosion of softer sedimentary rock that first surrounded them.

Tuff Stuff

Americans call the unusual rock formations at right hoodoos, but they are also known by a host of local terms around the world. In France they are *demoiselles coiffées* (ladies with elegant hairdos). To some Europeans, they are "earth pyramids"; to others, they are "tent rocks." But for centuries, locals in the Nevsehir province of Turkey's historic Cappadocia region have called the fanciful forms at right "fairy chimneys."

The rock spires resemble mushrooms after a growth spurt, and some of them tower more than 100 feet high. They are formed of tuff, a type of volcanic ash ejected during an eruption and then compacted in a process termed consolidation. The dark "caps" on many of the formations are made of denser, less porous rock, such as basalt, that is less likely to erode over the years than the soft tuff beneath it.

Tuff is often mistaken for tufa, a different form of soft rock that also erodes into unusual vertical formations. But tufa, unlike tuff, is not volcanic in origin.

Early inhabitants of Cappadocia sheltered in humble dwellings carved into the spires; later, Byzantine Christians carved Orthodox churches into the rock. Some residents of the region's main city of Goreme live in lavishly decorated caverns inside the chimneys, and luxury hotels offer rooms with a view—of erosion's fantastic architecture.

A climber ascends a radiant hill of ice in the Mendenhall Ice Caves near Juneau, Alaska.

H₂OMG!

Water is a shape-shifter, moving among three states: liquid, vapor and ice. Although it is featured in this chapter, water pervades this entire book: it's in the clouds that shape the weather, in the perfect geometry of snowflakes, in the bubbling geysers and prismatic mineral springs of tectonic hot spots. Water bends sunlight into rainbows, takes shape as mighty icebergs—and is part of Dylan Thomas's "force that through the green fuse drives the flower." Water is sparse only in the highest reaches of the atmosphere, amid the chilly realms of the auroras.

Water vapor is the most common component of volcanic gases. Water covers 71% of Earth's surface—and composes 50% to 65% of your body, depending on your age. "Thousands have lived without love," the poet W.H. Auden wrote, "not one without water."

Realms of Ice

When water abandons its liquidity, fantastic forms take shape

Alone in a Frozen World

Ice caves are among nature's most eerie places: caverns within structures composed of frozen water and thus far more ephemeral than terra firma. The diver above is exploring an ice cave filled with seawater in Antarctica. Above the diver are holes punched in the ice crust by Weddell seals (*Leptonychotes weddellii*); thinner than the rest of the ice layer, these areas are radiant with sunlight.

The starfish on the bottom of the cavern, *Odontaster validus,* may look decorative, but their business in this place is much more primordial: they feed on feces left by the seals. Thus this lovely picture illuminates both the physics of water and the interdependence of species.

Close Encounters

Locals in Ferryland, Newfoundland, are familiar with icebergs: they live in a coastal area of the Atlantic Ocean called "Iceberg Alley," where buoyant islands of ice often cruise by after being calved from glaciers or ice fields in Greenland and farther north. But the monster above didn't pass through: it grounded itself near shore in mid-April 2017 and quickly became a tourist attraction. Residents said it was one of the largest icebergs they had ever seen. (The proximity of the iceberg to the shore shown in the photo above is real—it was not exaggerated by a telephoto lens.)

We've all been told that icebergs are deceptive, for the part that's underwater is far more massive than the portion that's above the waves. But seeing is believing, and German photographer Tobias Friedrich took the plunge for the rest of us, diving some 90 feet deep into the frigid waters of Tasiilaq Fjord in East Greenland to capture the immensity of one berg's bottom.

Watering Holes

Exploring the wonders of cenotes, blue holes, grottoes and atolls

Notable Cenote

Recipe for a cenote: take a sinkhole created by karst topography, add a reservoir of clear rainwater and perhaps a trickling waterfall, and illuminate with a brilliant shaft of light that enters through a natural oculus. Result: bliss.

Mexico's Yucatán Peninsula is one of the most cenote-rich regions in the world, thanks to its terrain of soft limestone, which is riddled with pits and caverns that expose natural groundwater. The term "cenote" is derived from a Maya word—*ts'onot*—that roughly translates as "sacred well." But as for the hushed, magical mood evoked by shifting sunlight and rippling water in this subterranean pleasure dome: that's indescribable.

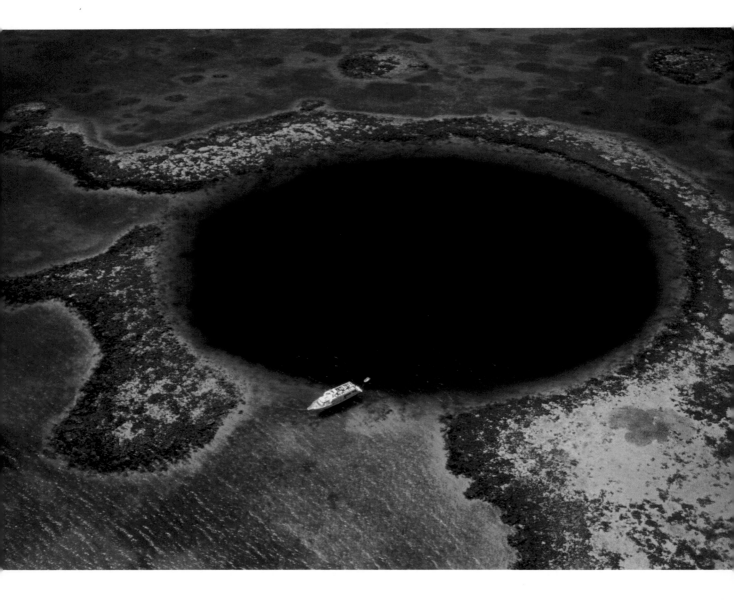

Bull's-eye!

Think of a blue hole as a cenote that went to sea. The geological processes that form these deep shafts or pits in areas of otherwise shallow ocean waters are similar to those behind a cenote: a sinkhole opens in the soft floor of the ocean, creating a natural well that cries out for exploration by dazzled scuba divers.

Indeed, it was the pioneering co-inventor of the Aqua-Lung, Jacques Cousteau, who in 1971 became the first person to explore the Great Blue Hole within Lighthouse Reef, about 60 miles offshore of Belize in the Caribbean Sea. The vertical shaft is just shy of 1,000 feet in diameter and is some 410 feet deep.

Tangled Up in Blue

Floating on the pellucid waters of the famed Blue Grotto on the
island of Capri, a rowboat seems suspended in a sapphire sea.
The science behind the illusion is not complex: the interior of the
grotto—a cave that holds water—is illuminated by two sources,
the small opening at sea level through which the boat entered
the cave, and an unseen shaft beneath the water's surface that
admits light, turning the saltwater into a pool of radiant azure.
The result is one of the planet's most beloved natural wonders,
a favorite of both modern tourists and the Roman emperor
Tiberius, once the ancient grotto's proud proprietor.

Volcanic Echoes

Atolls are among the most unusual and captivating features of tectonic geology. These mid-ocean structures are annular, or ring-shaped, reefs surrounding a central lagoon. The striking string of atolls at left is found in the Maldives, a nation composed of some 1,200 islands arranged into more than 20 atolls in the Indian Ocean southwest of the Indian subcontinent. The word "atoll" is based on the indigenous Dhivehi language's *atholhu*, a term that describes an administrative region rather than a geological formation.

It was English scientist Charles Darwin who, after investigating the phenomena of atolls on his 1831–36 voyage aboard the H.M.S. *Beagle*, first proposed the theory that atolls take shape as reefs growing around a volcanic island. If the island sinks beneath the waves but the reef continues to grow, an atoll is formed. The astonishingly uniform line of atolls at left is thus the geological residue of a column of ancient eruptions.

The Science of Atolls

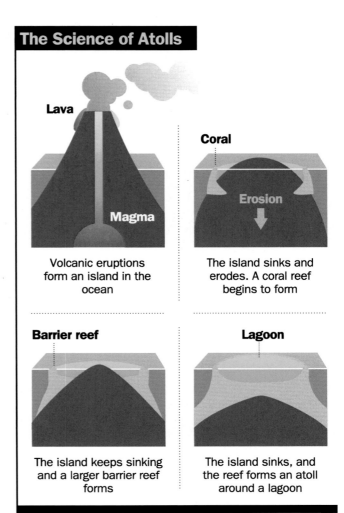

Volcanic eruptions form an island in the ocean

The island sinks and erodes. A coral reef begins to form

The island keeps sinking and a larger barrier reef forms

The island sinks, and the reef forms an atoll around a lagoon

Alternative Lakes

These lakes aren't mistakes—they're just natural outriders

Transitory Lake

Now you see it; now you don't. Transforming along with the seasons, Gruener See (Green Lake) in Tragoess, Austria, is a smallish body of water in late summer and fall, covering some five acres at a shallow depth of about three feet. But when spring arrives and the snow melts in the Hochschwab Mountains that surround Tragoess, Green Lake floods with cold, crystal-clear waters and swells to cover double its size, at a depth of almost 40 feet.

Braving the cold, office worker and amateur diver/photographer Marc Henauer visited Green Lake in the spring and captured pictures that show park benches and other summer facilities under its surface. "The sun created fantastic light rays through the water," he told Britain's *Daily Mail*. "[My] pictures were taken in natural light without using a flash.... The visibility is just incredible."

Spot the Lake?

What color is a lake? If you're describing Lake Hillier, on an island off Australia's southwest coast, above, the answer is: pink. The weird, double-take lake is a result of interactions among algae, bacteria and the lake's salty water.

Spotted Lake, near Osoyoos in British Columbia, is also a saline lake. Its richly colorful mineral deposits, left, are revealed in late summer, when most of its water dries up.

Waves and Tides

The power of water in motion creates memorable effects

Surf's Down

Thor's Well is a sort of upside-down waterspout whose rocky circumference is exposed at low tide and then disappears as high tides roll in and the well seems to swallow the waves that drift into its spiral maw. Although it's sensationally photogenic and evocative of an underworld portal, the natural feature is less fearsome than it appears to be. Located near the Pacific shore at Oregon's Cape Perpetua Scenic Area, it most likely began as a sea cave whose top and bottom both collapsed, leaving it to operate as a sort of oceangoing, tidal geyser. At high tide, its cycle is predictable: fill, spout, drain, repeat.

Is Thor's Well dangerous? Perhaps in a way you might not expect. As Vicki Penwell, a lead field ranger with the local Siuslaw National Forest, explained to the *Oregonian* newspaper, visitors often become entranced by the formation's roiling activity at high tide, only to be taken by surprise by "sneaker waves" that catch them from behind and sweep them off their feet, onto the rocks or into the drink. Landlubbers!

Wrong-Way Waves

Earth's tides respond to the gravity of both the moon and the sun, and some unusual results can occur when the gravitational imperative meets planetary topography. In a tidal bore, a surge during high tide sends waters rushing upstream, against a body of water's normal current, often with a leading wave so tall it can be surfed. Such bores (the word comes from the Middle English for "swell" or "wave") are often accompanied by turbulent waters and a loud, rushing noise.

At top, surfers ride a tidal bore along the River Garonne in France; at left, paddleboarders catch a wave from Alaska's best-known bore tide, at the Cook Inlet's Turn-again Arm, outside Anchorage.